Oh! What a Lovely Lockdown!

A SOCIAL DISTANCING ADVENTURE FOR CHILDREN

BY DR VIJAYTHA MURALI

This edition first published in the United Kingdom 2020
ISBN: 978-1-910853-21-4

Published by:
LionessPublishing.com

ILLUSTRATED BY
HULLO CREATIVE

hullocreative.com

In support of:

the national charity for sick children
WellChild is a Charity Registered in England and Wales 289600 and Scotland SC045010.
Company Number 1815689.

FOREWORD

by

Oliver Phelps

WellChild Ambasador

"Oh! What a lovely Lockdown" couldn't have come at a better time. Vijaytha has created such a timely, engaging children's book that will entertain children and parents alike, and hopefully help them through these strange times. Being a twin myself, I particularly connected with the characters of Lily and Leo who re-mphasise the importance of family, connection and creativity in challenging periods;

I'm sure these characters will make a memorable mark on their readers.

As an ambassador for WellChild, the national charity for sick children, I welcome the support Vijaytha is giving to the charity by donating profits. I am certain that this book will help uplift, and encourage imagination and creativity of children through lockdown and beyond.

Acknowledgements

To my family, for always emphasising the importance of finding happiness within the family unit no matter what the circumstance.

To all my wonderful friends who have been instrumental in encouraging me to challenge myself and to express my creativity - your support means everything.

To my colleagues in healthcare who are constantly striving to keep everyone safe with strength, patience and tenacity. .

Finally, to all those at Lioness Publishing, WellChild, Hullo Creative, Visibility Creator and to Louise Cummins, whose passion and dedication has helped me in bringing this book to life.

Vijaytha x

Oh! What a Lovely Lockdown!

A SOCIAL DISTANCING ADVENTURE FOR CHILDREN

BY DR VIJAYTHA MURALI

Twins Lily and Leo were having a **terrible day!**

Their birthday party was **cancelled**.

Their summer holiday was **cancelled**.

Playdates with their best friends were **cancelled**.

Even school was **cancelled!**

"But why Mum?" Leo asked, angrily.

"Because of the Coronavirus." Mum said.

"We have to stay inside the house most of the time" she explained "It's called lockdown - it's to keep us all safe."

"This virus is **ruining everything!**" Lily cried.

"Don't worry, I think you're both going to find ways to have fun at home, - you just need to give it a good try!", said Mum.

"Does that mean we watch TV and play on our phones **every day**?" Leo asked. .

"Definitely not!" said Dad

"Here's what I'm going to do" he said, taking out a pen and notepad.

"I'm going to write you a list of things to try. One every day." he said. "And guess what! - you won't need a TV or a phone for any of these!"

Oh! What a Lovely Lockdown!

ACTIVITY DAY 1: COOKING

On the first day, their task was to pick out their favourite recipe and make it - **all by themselves**!

"I know!" Leo said - "We can make chocolate chip cookies!"

"What a great idea!" shouted Lily, excitedly.

One by one, they gathered all the ingredients - they breathed in the sugary smells, felt the trickle of the butter running through their hands and tasted the sweetness of the chocolate.

In no time, the warm, sticky and delicious cookies were ready - **they had so much fun.**

"These cookies are delicious!" said Dad.

"We've learned how much fun cooking is!" said Leo.

"Making food at home can bring the family **so much happiness!**" Mum smiled with pride.

"Yes! So much!" Lily grinned as they dug into the delicious cookies.

7

ACTIVITY DAY 2: SINGING

Lily and Leo couldn't wait to see what the next activity was! "Learn a new song" it read.

"I know!" Lily said "we could learn a song from our favourite movie!"

Word by word, with music blasting in the background, Lily and Leo learned not one, not two, but **three** songs!

They laughed and they sang at the top of their voices - **they had so much fun.**

"How brilliant!" said Dad.

"I never knew singing could make me this happy!" Lily said.

"Music is a fantastic way to **brighten your mood!**" Mum smiled.

"Yes it is!" Leo grinned.   And they spent all evening singing together.

ACTIVITY DAY 3: WRITING

Leo couldn't wait to see what was on the list the next day. "Writing" it read.

"I know!" Leo said, "Let's write all about the coronavirus lockdown!"

They both raced to get pens and paper and chatted all about the lockdown before they started - all the fun they had had, but also the times things had felt scary or sad.

Word by word, moving their pens up and down, they wrote long letters - **they had so much fun** and **felt so much better**.

They couldn't wait to show Mum and Dad what they had written!

"Writing is such a great way to help you **understand how you feel**". Mum smiled and gave them both a big hug.

"Yes it is" Lily and Leo agreed.

They folded up their letters and put them in their special boxes for memories which they kept safe under their beds.

ACTIVITY DAY 4: PAINTING

On the fourth day, Lily was excited to see that the activity read "painting"!

"I know!" Lily said, "Let's paint a picture of our family!"

With swishes, slushes and plenty of colours, they both painted beautiful pictures of Mum, Dad, Grandma, Grandad and themselves - together and happy - **they had so much fun**.

"How wonderful!" said Dad.

"Painting is a brilliant way to **use your imagination!** " Mum smiled.

"Yes it is!" - Lily and Leo both agreed.

They posted their paintings to grandma and grandad as a special surprise - **they were so proud of themselves!**

"This picture will remind them that we'll be together again soon!" Lily said excitedly.

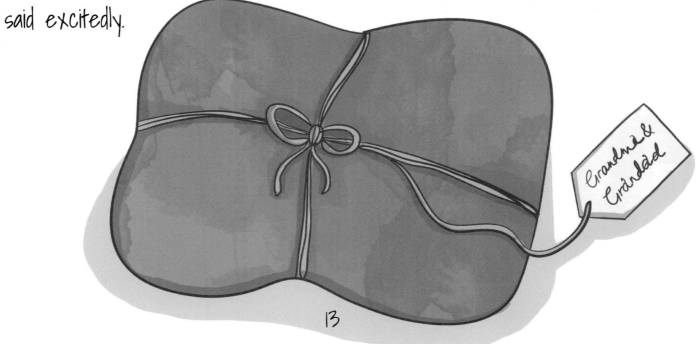

Activity Day 5: Spending time in Nature

Lily and Leo were confused. The next activity read "spending time in nature! "

"But I thought all the activities were going to be inside!" said Leo.

"Not exactly - I've saved you some surprises" winked Dad.

Together they walked, hand in hand through the park, up the sunny green hills and near the bright blue streams of water. **They were having so much fun!**

They even saw their friends in the distance! "Can we go and play with them?" asked Leo.

"Not yet" said Mum. "I know it's hard, but because of the coronavirus, you need to keep **at least a 2**

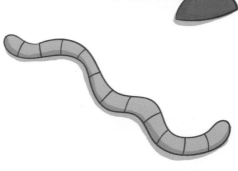

14

metre distance from all your friends, to keep everyone safe - you can wave to them though! " she smiled.

"We understand," said Lily. "At least we spent some time outside in the sun!!" she said.

"Getting some **fresh air always makes you feel better!**" said Mum.

"Yes it does!" Lily and Leo said.

15

Activity Day 6: Surprise

Lily and Leo looked at the list and saw the last activity simply read **"Surprise"**.

"Surprise?" Leo asked, looking at Lily puzzled.

"I'm not sure what we're meant to do" said Lily, looking equally puzzled.

They **couldn't wait** to ask Mum and Dad what it meant and ran as fast as they could to find them.

"Happy birthday Lily and Leo" Dad said as he switched on the computer.

"This is your surprise birthday party!"

Lily and Leo were shocked to see all their friends and family on the computer screen! They were smiling, laughing, waving and cheering - **it was wonderful!**

"We're all going to play musical bumps - dancing is the best way to celebrate - **you always feel happy when you dance!**" Mum said.

16

"And the best part about dancing is - **it doesn't matter whether you're inside or outside the house!**" Lily said, excitedly.

Song by song, they **sang**, they **danced** and they **laughed** the whole day long - **Lily and Leo had so much fun.**

17

Oh! What a Lovely Lockdown!

"Spending time at home in the lockdown **has been so much fun!**" said Leo.

"Because, we've been with you!" shouted Lily.

They both gave Mum and Dad big hugs - they were all safe together and that's what mattered the most.

"Oh, what a lovely lockdown!" said Mum, smiling.

Oh! What a Lovely Lockdown!

WHAT DO YOU WANT TO CREATE?

What would you like to cook, sing, write and paint? Write 3 of each below:

I WOULD LIKE TO COOK: ....

....

I WOULD LIKE TO SING: ....

....

I WOULD LIKE TO WRITE: ....

....

WHICH NATURE SPOT WOULD YOU LIKE TO VISIT?

....

WHAT THREE THINGS WOULD YOU LIKE ON YOUR SURPRISE WISH LIST?

1 ....

2 ....

3 ....

Lily and Leo
wish you
a lovely lockdown!

THE END!

ABOUT THE AUTHOR

Dr Vijaytha Murali is an acute medical physician at an NHS hospital in Birmingham, England. She graduated from Edinburgh Medical School in 2015.

Born in India, Vijaytha was three when she moved to the UK, where she grew up in Scotland surrounded by three generations of her family. She grew up hearing stories with depth, moral and meaning that her parents and grandparents used to recite to her and from that, gleaned lessons which continue to uplift her in challenging times.

As a front line medic during this time of the Covid-19 pandemic, Vijaytha sees first hand the effects of the illness on so many people, not least her friends and colleagues.

Vijaytha feels it is key to everyone's wellbeing at this time to stay connected, uplifted and happy. She is passionate about creativity and feels that the pandemic presents the opportunity for the exploration and nurturing of new skills.

Vijaytha wrote **"Oh! What a Lovely Lockdown!"** with the intention of connecting with the youngest minds in attempt to inspire an optimistic approach to restrictions of the pandemic. It is her hope that all readers will be able to connect with Lily and Leo and as a result, infuse excitement and creativity to help navigate this unprecedented time.

About WellChild

WellChild
the national charity for sick children

WellChild is the national charity for seriously ill children and their families. More than 100,000 children and young people are living across the UK with serious health needs.

Their families are delivering round-the-clock medical care behind closed doors. Many are reliant on external carers and are worried about the short and long term impacts COVID 19 will have on the wellbeing of their children..

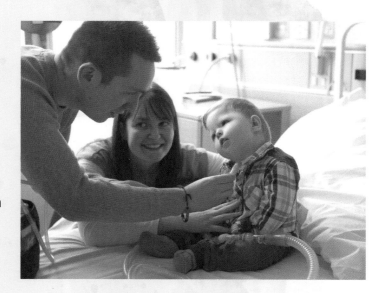

The pandemic poses some of the toughest challenges to these families; many of them will need to shield for prolonged periods of time within lockdown and beyond, making them feel more isolated and vulnerable then ever before.

WellChild is responding and adapting its services to meet this sudden and growing need by:

1. Helping families get essential supplies through the WellChild COVID-19 Response Team.
www.wellchild.org.uk/coronavirus/direct-response

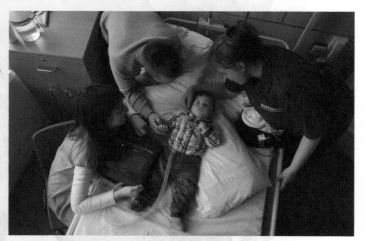

2. Connecting families across the UK for mutual support, advice and friendship via the WellChild Family Tree.
www.wellchild.org.uk/connecting-families/

3. Publishing information, guidance, and resources specifically for families caring for medically complex children. A great example is Medicines for Children:
www.wellchild.org.uk/medicinesforchildren/

4. Raising greater public awareness of the key issues facing families.
www.wellchild.org.uk/notanurse_but/

5. Many WellChild Nurses are also adapting their services to safely support the families on their caseloads.
www.wellchild.org.uk/wellchild-nurses/

Thank you for purchasing this book to help WellChild give this vulnerable population the best chance to thrive through this crisis – properly supported at home, with their families.

To find out more about WellChild and the work they do visit www.wellchild.org.uk.